SECRETS OF SUCCESSFUL DENTISTS

DR LEONARD J MAGUIRE

*BDS MFDS RCSED MFGDP MDTFED AFFMLM LL.M MBA CMGR MCMI
PG DIP. MED.ED. FICD*

DR DEREK J MAGUIRE

BDS MDTFED FFGDP(UK) FDS RCPS(GLAS) FICD

To Lauren and Muriel,
for always supporting, encouraging and inspiring us
in all we do.

Design by Velin@Perseus-Design.com

ISBN: 978-1-5272-3782-7

"The P.A.C.E Method"

1. Timing Is Key   **2.** Demonstrate the Problem   **3.** Contrast Principle   **4.** 'The Money Chat'   **5.** Question Time   **6.** Take Action

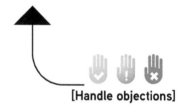

[Handle objections]

Follow this proven 6-step method to:

- **P:** Discuss your treatment **plans** comfortably (including the 'money' part)

- **A: Accelerate** your dentist-patient connection, deliver true value, increase profits

- **C:** Be confident you have obtained valid, informed **consent**

- **E:** Manage your patient **expectations** predictably

Contents

"You can have everything in life you want if you will just help enough other people get what they want."

- Zig Ziglar

Chapter 1

Introduction

———•———

Fellow Ambitious Dentist,

It's never been more important to educate yourself – after dental school.

And keep educating yourself.

Especially in non-clinical areas.

There isn't a quick or easy way.

It's going to have to come from you.

First and foremost – congratulations and big respect.

You have proved by reading this 6-Step method that you are serious and motivated to improve your life and the lives of your patients.

Now, I have invested a lot of time, study and my own hard-earned money in creating this for you.

It has been created to a high level, to the absolute best of my ability.

I've used some of my best training from my Master of Business Administration and Master of Medical Law and Ethics in here.

(Never mind my dental knowledge from working within our family-owned, group of 10 General Dental Practices)

And whilst that's great.

And _very_ reassuring for you.

Here's the single biggest and relevant benefit to be really excited about…

It is tried and tested, by myself, and also the dentists I work with.

But this material is not taught anywhere else.

I have never revealed this publicly before now.

This is personal.

Naturally, there are some ground rules I recommend:

1. You have to take the time to invest in yourself and really get to grips with the structures processes behind this blueprint.

2. Action is the key – things won't be any different tomorrow if you don't do something different today. Make this that day.

3. Be resilient and willing to test. You have to test what works, but perhaps more importantly, learn from what doesn't. Take it on board, get up and go again. Be prepared for rejection (to begin with). But don't let it beat you. Success rarely comes quickly or

in the absence of hard work. This is not some sort of 'Get Rich Quick' plan.

Initially, consider 'The XOX Method' on page 5 – which is really all about the habits you form in the surgery.

But not with your hands.

Rather, the skills you possess with your words and how you communicate them.

Ultimately this will determine the success you enjoy.

Bonus Chapter 2

XOX Thinking

In any business or organisation, irrespective of what or where you work, there are 3 key areas to always focus on.

As follows:

> 1 - Systems and processes
> 2 - The people
> 3 - Outcomes and results

But here's the problem...

Many people / businesses function as **OXO**, as follows:

O Ordinary Systems / Processes
X Extraordinary People (or dentists)
O Ordinary Results

Sure, you might get someone who is a brilliant dentist individually.

But without the best systems or processes behind them, their success will ultimately never reach its true potential.

For example:

O: Whilst the Northern Ireland football team are famous for their spirit and effort, they are relatively ordinary in terms of quality.

X: George Best was a phenomenal footballer from Northern Ireland. Arguably the best in the world at times. He even has an airport named after him (George Best Belfast City Airport).

O: But he never won the world cup. Because the facilities, system and team around him weren't able to match his quality.

Therefore, I urge you to break the mould, be ambitious, and aim to completely reverse this process.

Aim for **XOX**:

X Extraordinary Systems / Processes
O Ordinary People/Dentists
X Extraordinary Results

With extraordinary systems in place, relatively ordinary dentists, can and will experience extraordinary success.

This is what was used as the foundation for "The P.A.C.E Method".

Enabling you to have conversations with your patients about:

- Treatments plans
- Their investment involved
- Managing expectations
- Gaining proper consent

Whilst at the same time, ensuring you have informed and valid consent – with engaged patients who are actively involved in their decision-making process and value your time and expertise (so, so important in our profession today).

If you could do this, with relative ease and predictability, would your daily life in practice be so much more enjoyable?

By the way – I class myself as a relatively ordinary, 'normal' dentist.

I work in General Practice.

Sure, I have my business, legal and teaching/consultancy roles – that I am more experienced in than my 'wet-fingered' dentistry.

But I am not a *clinical* Consultant.

And I don't hold any specific clinical speciality qualifications.

So the clinical work I carry out does not pretend to be anything other than that aimed at General Dental Practice.

Which I am more than happy with.

To be honest, I feel that General Dental Practice should be considered a speciality in its own right.

For example – any orthodontists and oral surgeons I know don't make dentures, crowns or treat root canals.

Similarly, you're not expected to do what they are experienced and qualified to do.

I'm fiercely protective and proud of working in General Dental Practice.

Consider this - if you are not comfortable with the thought of 'sales' – that is ok.

Just be sure this mindset is not impacting the treatments you offer (or indeed *how* you offer them).

Many people talk about 'Ethical Sales' or 'Upselling' in general business, as well as dentistry.

Personally, I don't believe there is any need to use these specific words.

Firstly – we should never feel like we are 'selling' treatments. That's not comfortable for anyone involved.

Secondly – I don't think there is any need to highlight the word 'ethical'.

Surely, as dentists, behaving in an 'ethical' manner should be assumed in everything we practice?

So, if like me, you don't want to feel as though you are selling (or 'ethically upselling' etc, etc) – follow The P.A.C.E Method.

Remember, you don't need to convince your patients about anything.

You just need to have the confidence in your abilities to be convincing, to enable you to deliver treatment options, and the value of what you do, in a way your patients understand.

Big difference.

Why not re-phrase the word 'upsells' in your own mind, to **"Upgrades"**.

A long time ago, that shift in mindset really helped me.

The 6 Steps to follow?

Here we go!

1. **Timing is Key**

2. **Demonstrate the Problem**

3. **The Contrast Principle**

4. **'The Money Chat'**

5. **Question Time**

6. **Take Action**

Here is an absolutely crucial part of the process…

(Possibly the most important bit)

This sequence <u>must</u> be carried out following this exact order.

I've tested it, and you've guessed it, it doesn't work any other way.

Each of the steps must follow in this order starting with 1 (Timing is Key) and finishing with 6 (Take Action).

More on that later.

But for now, just remember:

Use *every* stage.

Always, always, always in this PRECISE order.

"There is no free lunch. Don't feel entitled to anything you don't sweat and struggle for. If you see a need, don't ask, 'Why doesn't somebody do something?' Ask instead, 'Why don't I do something?' The world needs more shepherds and fewer sheep. Don't be afraid of taking risks or being criticized. If you don't want to be criticized, don't say anything at all, don't do anything, and don't be anything. Don't be afraid to fail."

- Marian Wright Edelman

Chapter 3

Step One - Timing is Key

All of this has to begin at the current/initial appointment/consultation.

That could be the routine check-up, emergency pain appointment, fractured filling/tooth etc.

Whatever reason your patient is in front of right now.

This is when to follow through the 6-step process of The P.A.C.E Method.

Don't take the bitewings and 'let them know the findings at their next appointment'.

Don't place a dressing in a tooth that you intend to crown, without having the discussion of what's involved with crowns.

State the problem when they are there with you on the day.

Remember, your patient may not necessarily be aware there is a problem.

They may not necessarily be suffering any symptoms.

Be very careful with the language that you use at this stage.

Take care to avoid colloquialisms or jargon.

This can diminish the perceived relevance or importance of any treatments you discuss.

For example, at home in Northern Ireland, it is not uncommon to hear people talk about a 'wee' something.

E.g. Would you like a wee coffee?

Will we go for a wee walk?

You need a 'wee' root canal.

Your patient may not realise that root canals don't always settle.

Some end up being extracted.

And that's despite 4-5 root canal appointments.

And after the tooth has been extracted, you could be asked whatever became of the that 'wee root canal'.

You and I understand root canals can be sclerosed, vertical fractures can appear, files can separate.

But remember – dentistry is **our** first language.

Not our patients' first language.

What is obvious to us, is not always obvious to patients when discussing dental matters.

Best not to assume anything.

Now, on another note, this first appointment also provides another hidden opportunity.

And that opportunity is for rapport building.

One of the most significant areas that great dentists excel in, is rapport building.

Of course, some are more natural than others.

I'm sure you can think of a few examples – the dentists who can build rapport without even appearing to try or realising.

But it's important to recognise the value in this skill.

And invest the time, energy and money in learning and improving this if needed.

Bear in mind the *lifetime value* of a patient.

And not simply in terms of financial value to your practice.

Consider how many referrals are made by current patients recommending you.

Whatever perceived 'cost' you may have held about investing in personal or business growth, will not even come close to the potential that lies within your patient list – especially if your patients know, like and trust you.

Remember, rapport building = trust building.

You may have heard me say this before – but patients don't tend to complain about or sue dentists they like.

And rapport building is not restricted to patients alone.

This can involve colleagues, managers, suppliers, nurses, receptionists, technicians, engineers to name a few.

Really, it's just treating people how you would want to be treated yourself.

For now, follow **these 5 key steps for Rapport Building:**

1. Be prepared with questions
2. Take a genuine interest in your patients' lives (not just their teeth!)
3. Ask better quality questions (more on this later)
4. Listen carefully (two ears, one mouth – use them in that proportion)
5. Take the time to get to know your patients personally.

Good example topics for rapport building?

Use **FOHO** to make conversations with patients:

Family
Occupation
Holidays
Other e.g. hobbies, pets, topical news articles, common interests.

RAPPORT ➜ TRUST (the foundation upon which relationships are built) ➜ REFERRALS (from similar people)

We'll go into this much deeper in your second BONUS (chapter 12) at the end which is entirely dedicated to Building Rapport.

Action Notes:

_____

_____

_____

_____

_____

_____

_____

_____

_____

_____

_____

_____

_____

"You can't finish what you don't start, and you should never start what you're not committed to finish."

- Gary Ryan Blair

Chapter 4

Step Two -
Demonstrate the Problem

What are the benefits of being really effective at this Demonstration/ Presentation Stage?

In a nutshell, you make it far easier for you to get across your ideas to patients and easier for them to understand your ideas.

Even further - <u>a demonstration</u> is much more powerful than <u>a presentation</u>.

So we need something to help show our patients exactly what we are talking about.

Showing them their radiographs and discussing what you see (normal and abnormal) will help.

But remember – patients do not have a clue what a radiograph is.

I remember when we attended an appointment for a scan when my wife was pregnant with Sophia.

We were chatting away to the Consultant throughout.

He knew we are dentists – we were all interested in what he was looking at and where.

Just as any soon-to-be parents are.

But because we are dentists, he assumed we knew from the scan what the sex of our baby was.

Let's be clear, I have absolutely no idea what we were looking at in those scans!

But you go along with the flow.

I know I did.

And really, all we wanted to know was that he (the Consultant) was happy with what all he saw.

Are dental radiographs really much different when being explained?

Patients aren't trained to know what to see on a bitewing.

Ultimately, they're most interested in knowing:

A) All's well

Or

B) If there's a problem, what are you going to do to help them.

But showing them and talking through the findings can certainly help.

Of course, demonstration models can help as well (often a lab will be willing to provide), with example crowns, bridges, implants & dentures etc.

So they can really grasp what you are explaining looks like - how big or small it is, the shape, the shade/colour.

But the single best (and arguably most time and cost-effective) piece of equipment I have?

My **intra-oral camera**.

Total game-changer.

Now I am no photographer.

Not by a long stretch!

But I can only describe it as invaluable.

Why is that?

It allows you to take a picture of their actual problem/tooth in question.

It's personal to them.

They will remember that image when leaving... or perhaps you could print it off and give it home with them.

And in terms of managing expectations – that is very significant.

You and I know looking at a deep restoration "that just might not settle, we could be looking at root canal treatment here".

But that is in no way obvious to patients.

This will massively reduce the potential for complaints as well.

Think of a root canal example.

If you show them how deep you need to drill, where the canals are, how much tooth is left etc… well, at least they will know.

Remember to record all these conversations in your clinical notes.

Then, if all settles and goes to plan, you're great.

But if it doesn't settle, it can seem as though almost predicted it might not.

Either way, patient expectations have been managed successfully.

Compare that to not demonstrating fully the extent of the cavity, sclerosed canals etc.

They could leave thinking it's only a 'wee filling' or a 'wee root canal'.

If this doesn't settle, then it is possible you could seem to blame in some way.

When in reality, the only fault is perhaps mis-managing their expectations.

And there are many other benefits to taking clinical photographs.

A picture really does say 1000 words – and from a dento-legal stance, some clinical photographs often help your record keeping (if the dreaded complaint arrives).

For example:

- Demonstrating calculus build up
- Illustrating broken teeth/fillings
- Recording deficient crown margins
- Help locating canals during RCT
- Lumps and bumps being referred onward
- Anything and everything

If I were to advise you to purchase any piece of equipment, I could not recommend an intra-oral camera highly enough.

They don't need to be expensive.

In fact, in terms of dental equipment, they are relatively inexpensive.

But I couldn't begin to calculate the benefits of the investment.

Bonus Tip:

When performing any treatment.

Be that a crown prep, fillings, root canal therapy…. whatever it may be.

I'd urge you to take photographs at a relevant stage:

1. Before you start
2. During the procedure e.g. caries removed
3. At the end

Then, once you have finished, take a few minutes at the end to show them to your patient.

That way, they can see exactly how much/little tooth you have to work with, and how challenging it can be.

They will be able to compare before, during and after.

And whilst managing their expectations brilliantly, they will feel involved and that you genuinely care.

It also provides a great opportunity to build rapport.

(Remember, people don't tend to sue people they like or trust. The same applies to dentists and patients).

Again, this is really just about getting into the habit of doing this.

I wouldn't carry out even the simplest of fillings any other way.

The same process every time.

Personal Point - What do I do?

I take clinical photographs all the time!

Virtually every patient.

Whether it's for:
- Check-up
- Emergency/pain appointment
- Fractured restoration or tooth
- Periodontal disease / calculus / recession
- Sub-optimal crown margins
- Length of gap span if missing teeth
- Tooth surface loss
- Vertical fractures
- During root canal treatment
- Etc etc. you get the idea

As well as that...

With every treatment, I tend to take and show the following photographs:

- Before (e.g. the broken tooth/restoration before you start)
- During (e.g. the caries underneath)
- After (e.g. the final composite restoration)

Why is that?

Simply – it demonstrates the problem/issue, <u>their</u> problem.

And therefore...

- **Manages expectations** – e.g. longevity of tooth anticipated, post-op pain etc.
- Aids you should any dreaded **dento-legal** implications arise
- Raises the quality of your **record keeping**

○ And it's just **very good practice** – keeping your patient involved and **engaged by building value, trust and rapport.**

Remember clinical photographs don't replace radiographs. Rather, they should be seen as an adjunct.

Action Notes:

_____

_____

_____

_____

_____

_____

_____

_____

_____

_____

_____

_____

"It's not the employer who pays the wages. Employers only handle the money. It's the customer who pays the wages."

- Henry Ford

Chapter 5

Step Three -
The Contrast Principle

In the absence of contrast, everything sounds either expensive, or cheap.

But you don't know which.

Invariably, options exist.

But you know the 'best' or most appropriate one.

How do you explain that comfortably and confidently to your patient?

By using "The Contrast Principle"

The Contrast Principle

As I said, "Without contrast, everything sounds expensive, or cheap!"

Unfortunately, your patients don't know which one it is either.

So, we have got to gather information or make statements or demonstrate - in order to position the price (see Step 4 – 'The Money Chat').

You position your price based on contrast between the financial and emotional impact of the current situation against the price of your solution.

This is how you stop most (not all) of the unnecessary price objections that can arise.

Why do they come about?

Often the price has not been correctly framed or positioned by what you are saying and doing (before you begin to mention the money).

In other words, what you **mean** to say **before** you say it.

A lot of people can get bogged down by the *features* and *benefits* of their products or service.

It's how we are trained – what does something <u>do</u>, how does it <u>work</u> etc.

And whilst these are important, we need to consider the outcomes and transformation associated with what we can do as dentists.

Patient decisions are based on emotion and then backed up with logic.

Think of how what you can offer and do as a dentist will impact your patients' lives.

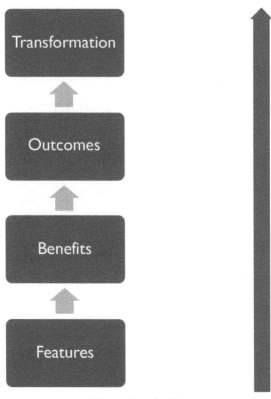

Hierarchy of selling

For example, a composite filling on a posterior tooth (instead of amalgam):

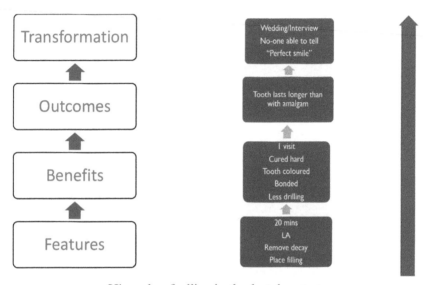

Hierarchy of selling in the dental context

Features & Benefits

Features = what something has or is.

Benefits = what it does for the patient (solves a problem or capitalises on an opportunity for them).

When talking about benefits, we must make sure we are using matching benefits.

Think about the benefits you must match in order to resonate with them.

- *Feature (state this)*
- *Benefit (link to this)*
- *Question*

For example:

- ○ It has or is this…
- ○ So you can have this/enjoy this/are…
- ○ Does that sound like something you'd be open to?

How will my product or service create peace of mind with my patients?

Peace of mind is a key driver for people.

How will my product or service make people feel better about themselves?

What are the problems my product or service solves for my patient?

What do they want most? Can only have one answer.

Why do they want it? This is where they emotionalise it.

What will stop them buying it?

Being able to answer these questions will give so much insight into what our patients want.

Why People Buy?

Generally, people buy to fulfil one or more of the following 7 psychological needs:

1. To be rich
2. To be admired
3. To be healthy
4. Prestige
5. Social Status
6. Power or Influence
7. To be on the cutting edge

But here's the key thinking behind this - ALL buying decisions are emotional.

Deciding to proceed with a particular treatment plan is a buying decision for your patients.

People buy for the desire for gain (towards motivation) or for the fear of loss (away motivation).

People will buy more often to avoid pain than they will to gain pleasure.

Away motivation is much more likely to cause action taking.

People are not interested in buying a service/product like a health insurance plan.

They are interested in what that service/product will <u>do</u> for them.

Patients are no different.

Why would anyone want a root canal?

They wouldn't.

But they would want to be free from pain.

People, or patients, don't buy treatments they buy the **benefits** of treatments.

There is always one key benefit above all others that makes your patient want to buy.

There is always one major objection that holds someone back from buying.

You must uncover the major benefit and handle the major objection to 'close the sale' – and ensure your patient receives the best possible treatment.

Action Notes:

"Success is neither magical nor mysterious. Success is the natural consequence of applying basic fundamentals."

- Jim Rohn

Chapter 6

Step Four - 'The Money Chat'

Now we come to the 'money part' of the discussion with your patient.

Honestly, this is the part most dentists admit to struggling with.

I was no different.

But we are not taught on how to discuss fees with patients in dental school.

And so, you can feel it in the room when you first do this – it's awkward.

When really, it needs to be smooth, confident and comfortable.

Make yourself the prize.

Are they not fortunate to have you as their dentist?

Value yourself, your time, your ability.

The difference you can make to someone's life.

This could be a much greater impact than you even realise.

Opening a tooth for a root canal is a relatively routine task for you and me.

But as a patient, they could be in the worst pain of their life.

Now, on to another important area.

Discounts…

Don't start randomly discounting in your head.

You have invested heavily (time and money) in your education and learning – often we, as dentists, do not place a high enough value on that.

We really do have the ability to make a significant difference to people's lives.

Use *The Contrast Principle* for pricing, similar to when contrasting options of treatments.

Must discuss fees – but at the appropriate time.

Biggest mistake I see?

Dentists can have a tendency to want to get started with the 'hands-on' part of dentistry.

And so, the 'money part' can come too soon in the conversation.

"Treatment before diagnosis is malpractice"

Same theory applies to the flow and structure involved here.

You shouldn't start discussing what the options are to restore the tooth, and how much it will cost, until your patient fully understands what the problem is.

(Remember – a quick photograph with your intra-oral camera is invaluable here. A picture really does speak 1000 words).

Don't be afraid to acknowledge a specific treatment plan being more expensive.

Sometimes, things can be 'reassuringly expensive'. For example, if someone offered you an apparently new iPhone for, say £50, what would your initial thought be?

Something isn't right here, of course.

It sounds too cheap to be true.

If it looks like a pig, and grunts like a pig, well… you know the rest.

Reassuringly expensive is a great mindset to have.

I always run the wife or granny test in my mind – if my wife or granny came in as this patient, what is the best possible and most appropriate option I could provide them with?

Then, have I provided this option in a clear way that they understand?

I tend to provide the options and finish with the one I recommend.

Careful not to confuse folks with unrealistic options or jargon.

The money part must be honest, clear and easy to understand.

No ambiguity.

Don't be afraid to offer your recommendation.

I often say, "If it were my wife's tooth, I would…"

This is reassuring for patients to hear.

Obviously, you would want to provide what is best for your spouse.

It helps them to justify their decision – especially if it is not the cheapest option.

Ultimately, the price is only one of the factors used as part of your patient's decision-making process.

A factor, not the factor.

Action Notes:

_____

_____

_____

_____

_____

_____

_____

_____

_____

_____

_____

_____

"The art of the sale is an emotional experience. They are looking for a transformation – something that will cause an improvement or makes their life a little easier."

- Dan Kennedy

Chapter 7

Handling Objections

Objections arise when there is not enough desire in order to make their decision.

So, we have to use the power of Away and Towards Motivation.

Away (pain) = catalyst for action, gets people started.

Towards (gain) = continuation of action, keeps people going.

Let's take a deeper look into this together.

Why do people object?

Variety of reasons.

Unfortunately, what happens is they object using statements rather than questions.

So, they say things like:

- I don't like red
- I couldn't afford it
- That sounds expensive

All of those objections are statement based.

What we need to do when we get one of these.

Initially, use the idea of The Contrast Principle to reduce number of objections.

Then, translate statement objections into questions

- **Get an objection**
- **Translate it to a question in our minds**
- **Check that translation accurate**
- **Then answer the question in our minds**
- **Close the sale / gain commitment for action**

What is the question they are really asking me?

Need to check before you answer that question, just in case you have translated.

Then once answered, we 'close the sale' i.e. gain commitment for action through proper informed consent.

As dentists, we have got to be very careful when 'closing'.

So - translate objections into questions.

Isolate the Objection

If it's possible.

And without sounding cheesy.

Can you find a way of asking your patient whether that's the only thing stopping them going ahead at the moment?

Always with integrity and honesty – that's assumed in our profession.

Ultimately trying to get best result for your patient.

Gentle voice and tones.

Very often, objections are subject to the amount of rapport you have with that patient.

Ask if you could solve that particular problem, would they be happy to go ahead then.

Therefore, you have isolated the objection.

Don't want one simple little objection to cloud the whole issue

The Timing of Handling the Objections

1. **Before.** I prefer, wherever possible, to handle objections before they are raised. When we do it before, we stop the other person (patient) digging themselves into a hole with that objection. Need

to get them out of the hole, before we can even get them to start to see a different view point.

"Hmm, that sounds expensive." Screwed up face, leaned back, folded arms etc.

Therefore, need to be aware of the likely objections that are going to come up, work out how we are going to handle them within in the gathering and presenting stages, so that they are not likely to be even raised.

Bring it up yourself. Shows you are strong and have considered it.

2. **Immediately.** Need to handle it straightaway or else the objection will have an effect on everything else.

"I'd like to think about it!"

How many times have you heard that?

What do they *really* mean?

Sometimes this is really a "no" when people are just polite.

I would rather have a real yes or no, than a fake one.

You could ask:

"Sometimes, when people say I want to think about it, they really mean no.

Is that what you're saying to me?"

Look and listen.

And if the particular treatment isn't for them, it's not a problem.

It's important to understand what it is they want to think about.

Don't ask bluntly as this won't be answered properly.

Got to throw possibilities into the equation, was it the price? The delivery?

So, you are saying to them that the answer they are going to give is acceptable.

Most people are polite and courteous and don't want to offend you.

So, you need to let them off that emotional hook.

And tell you what they mean.

Invariably will be a statement objection.

Translate this to a question and adjust.

Action:

- ○ Need to write out a list of the top 10 objections you have.
- ○ Then translate those into questions.
- ○ Then practice how you will handle them.

Analyse everything.

Be forensic.

Action Notes:

_____

_____

_____

_____

_____

_____

_____

_____

_____

_____

_____

_____

_____

"The difference between a successful person and others is not a lack of strength, not a lack of knowledge, but rather a lack of will."

- Vince Lombardi

Chapter 8

Step Five - Question Time

Firstly, allow appropriate **time** for questions.

Remember – listening to the answers is as important as asking the questions.

Some of the best advice I was ever offered, was to **"ask better quality questions"**.

Watch out for not being asked the question really intended.

We see this all the time, not just in the surgery.

E.g. *Can I have a think about it?*

This often means – "I need more information".

Now, it can be that people need more time to process and justify a decision – to themselves or someone at home.

And of course, it depends on the nature of the treatment being discussed.

Implants tend to involve many more factors than standard restorations.

But everyone is different.

Don't take perceived rejection personally.

Your face won't fit with everybody.

No matter how friendly or skilled you believe you are.

Another example I see at home, Mrs M asks me:

"What are you doing on Thursday evening?"

That's not the real question!

So, definitely encourage questions!

The more information you can gather the more benefit it will be.

Treatment planning and obtaining consent is a two-way process.

And you, or indeed your patient, are allowed to change your minds.

Questions are essential to keep patients engaged and ensure they understand.

Importantly, they also help to establish their *needs and wants*, and any associated risks or opportunity.

Remember – never assume!

"Prescription before diagnosis is malpractice"

You must find out exactly what your patient needs and wants, before offering a solution to a problem they perhaps didn't even realise they had.

Doing all of this will further build rapport.

And where there is rapport, there is trust.

People (i.e. patients) don't tend to complain about people (dentists) they like.

Briefly, on the subject of rapport – remember to keep it:

- Genuine
- Authentic
- Enthusiastic
- Interested

Patient's will be able to smell it off you, if you really care, or if you're watching the clock until home time.

Be inquisitive!

For example:

When a patient enquires about tooth whitening, think 'what is the real reason behind this question?'

With tooth whitening, it is often an emotionally driven question.

Normally, someone is getting married, graduating, starting a new job etc.

Also, once you find this information out, make a note of it on their chart.

That way you will be able to recall and ask about the event in 6 months at their check-up.

Dentistry is a caring profession.

By taking the time to ask or answer questions appropriately, your patients will feel much more valued, involved and relaxed in your surgery.

Simply put:

Do good work and for the right reasons and your patients will stay and the money will follow and take care of itself.

Building rapport and trust in this way will reduce the number of rejections/objections and price resistance.

Take the time to talk _with_ your patients, not _to_ them.

Open vs Closed

Two main types of questions exist, which you may have heard of before.

Open and closed.

Here's my take on it…

Open:

These are questions that encourage the conversation to begin and keeps it flowing.

Often, this is where much of the 'selling' takes place.

The patient is selling the idea to themselves that something needs done to fix their tooth.

e.g. "Are you having any bother with your teeth or gums at the moment?"

"If I had a magic wand, what would you want me to be able to do for you and your smile?"

Closed:

In contrast, closed questions really only allow for a yes/no answer.

These types of questions can be very helpful when you need to know a specific answer, such as when establishing a diagnosis.

e.g. "Is it sore with hot things like coffee?"

"Does the pain keep you awake at night?"

So, overall, both do serve a purpose but perhaps at different stages in the treatment discussion and plan.

Listen and Observe

When asking or answering a question, be very attentive.

Watch your patient, their reaction and their body language.

Everyone should be comfortable.

Allow them time to think and process what you say.

Don't be tempted to jump in too quickly and finish their sentences or second guess what their response will be.

Silence, at times, is perfectly ok.

Be 100% present in the moment with them at this time.

Not distracted by phone calls, messages, typing your notes etc.

Try to maintain eye contact as much as possible.

The skill of being a great listener does take time and practice to master.

Like many aspects of dentistry, it's simple but not easy.

Action Notes:

_____

_____

_____

_____

_____

_____

_____

_____

_____

_____

_____

_____

"Happiness comes when you believe in what you're doing, know what you're doing, and love what you're doing."

- Brian Tracy

.

Chapter 9

Step Six - Take Action

Why is it that so many people don't 'close' a sale or 'end' a conversation as such?

1. They don't know how. Never bothered to learn the words so when it comes to that point in the conversation, suddenly they get all nervous about it and misrepresent themselves.

By the way – I've been there too. Nobody taught me how to discuss fees with patients in dental school. Never mind discuss fees in a way that feels comfortable and straightforward.

Have this concept in your mind – "you don't sell treatments, you allow people to buy"

How you position yourself in your own mind, that will dramatically change how you deal with someone in the selling conversation.

2. **They have not practiced.** Don't be winging it on the day and stuttering and stumbling into the close and wondering why they are not getting the conversions. Practice makes permanent.

3. **They fear rejection.** Firstly, you have to realise it's not you personally it's the proposition – dissociate it from you. Secondly, have your own rules for rejection. What has to happen for you to feel rejected. Set the bar so high that it's not likely to happen in your life.

4. **They have no belief in a product or service that they are offering.** Selling is the transfer of our belief to a potential patient. That's what the sales conversation is. Need to deal with them as though they have said yes, not as though they might say yes.

Sometimes, through my coaching, I have asked dentists the following question:

> "Who are the wealthiest taxi drivers?"

This is a serious question!

"They know the best roads"

"They work in the major cities"

"They charge higher fares"

None of the above.

The answer?

"They always book the return journey"

I've travelled to Birmingham, England (UK) quite a bit over the years with work.

Whilst there, I always use the same taxi driver (Nathan!).

He's an excellent driver.

Of course, he knows the best roads to avoid the traffic etc.

No, he's not the cheapest.

And he's a brilliant laugh – always got a story to tell.

But, without fail, he will always ask when and where I need collected to return to the airport when travelling back home again.

If you think about it, you almost always have to get a taxi back (unless you were meeting a friend / relative who had a car, or there was public transport that suited).

Maybe not a taxi, but a return journey of some sort.

But if you're getting a taxi from the airport, the chances are you're getting one back again when the trip is over.

And he books it there and then.

The same applies to when we're in our surgeries.

We should always try and book the return journey.

I ask them to stop with reception.

And name the person I want them to stop with.

Not "the girls at the desk".

Here's what I use to finish off any treatment plan discussion:

"That's great, if you stop with [Receptionist Name] at the desk and they will get that booked in and all organised for you."

They can of course still have a think about it.

They can of course change their mind, choose a different treatment, need to ask more questions.

And it will depend on what the treatment needed is.

i.e. If it is a few straightforward fillings, most people are happy to organise that there and then. Whereas, if it is something more complex, say involving implants, then they might want another appointment to discuss what's involved again.

Both are fine – and both benefit from a 'return journey' being arranged.

But with another 'return journey' in the diary, it shows a commitment and seriousness by both the patient and practice.

If this were a more normal business type of sales process, this might be comparable with the 'closing' stage of a sale.

Of course, that's not what we're doing – but the overall goal is more similar than first seems.

So, what are the other benefits of this 'closing' idea?

- You help your patient solve the problem they needed/wanted help with
- They get the result they want
- You get the result you want
- E.g. help a current patient or gain a new patient etc.
- Build a long-term relationship (relational clients, not transactional customers)

My take on it…

- Go slowly, take your time
- Create the climate in which ethical persuasion takes place
- Don't rush this stage
- Remember your relationship with your patient – you are the trusted professional

Action Notes:

"The difference between manipulation and persuasion is <u>intent</u>.

If your intent is to sell something to someone that they don't want, need, desire or worse, something that won't produce the outcome they want, you're a con man.

However, if your intent is to help someone get the results they want, then you should use every ethical sales strategy you can to close the sale."

- Dave Dee

Chapter 10

Worked Example

———— • ————

Say one of your patients, let's call them Mrs M, attends with:

- A fractured upper right first molar (UR6)
- Part of buccal cusp has broken (although not sub-gingival)
- Pre-existing MOD amalgam crumbling away
- No RCT in situ, normal vitality
- No symptoms, just a sharp edge cutting into their tongue

In this scenario, I would often place a direct composite restoration.

But that's just me.

I know some may say crown, some may say indirect composite etc.

And that's perfectly fine.

We're not debating the clinical options here.

Rather the fact that options exist to restore this tooth.

And how are you going to present these options?

Discuss the problem, manage your patient's expectations throughout?

Discuss the fees associated, obtain valid consent etc.?

Here's how I use The P.A.C.E Method in cases such as this.

Remember this is my take on it. I would urge you to really find a quiet space and think about the words and phrases you use when discussing treatments and presenting options.

What sounds 'normal' for one dentist may sound 'strange' to another.

Which is a good thing.

We're all different, but so are our patients.

Really, it's the overall structure and steps to adhere to with The P.A.C.E Method.

Work through some examples and make it your own.

1. Timing is Key

- Chatting as I work and take a look
- Building rapport – how is the family, work, holidays planned? A genuine interest.
- Appear to have all the time in the world, no rush, she is my priority.
- The process has started at this first appointment.

2. Demonstrate the Problem

- Take clinical photos throughout
- Ask them to come and share the screen with you
- To show them their tooth
- No jargon at all (I struggle with this at times too!)
- Explain your findings and their significance

3. Contrast Principle

- Use the Contrast Principle to describe the various options that exist
- Compare the benefits and risks
- Potential complications
- What all is involved 'hands-on' with each option
- What you recommend
- Bear in mind the potential emotional attachment and transformation that exists.
- Manage expectations throughout.

4. 'The Money Chat'

- Explain the price for each treatment (using the Contrast Principle again)
- Be crystal clear with how much each item will cost in terms of money
- Offer the reasoning behind why some options are more expensive – is it a purely aesthetic difference? Or is it a stronger material? Less invasive perhaps?
- Remember – at times, something can be reassuringly expensive
- Don't be quick to discount (but be sure to let them know if you do!)

- It's not your money or tooth – so disassociate yourself from the actual 'financial' aspect of the discussion.
- You are really just delivering options and value to the best of your ability to help your patient make the best choice for themselves.

[Handle Any Objections]

- Don't be defensive
- Remain calm, understanding and open-minded
- For example:
- "I understand that this option is more expensive, however it is the better option for your tooth in the long term?
- Some patients need more time to justify their decision (either to someone at home, or to themselves – your responsibility is to ensure they have all of the information needed to do this)

5. Question Time

- Not only ask, but actively listen to the answers given.
- "if it were my wife's tooth…"
- Reassure them if they pick the option you suggest
- Listen and look
- You don't need to *convince* anyone, simply be *convincing*.

6. Take Action

Questions I ask to "book the return journey" …
- Does that all make sense ok?
- Does that sound like something you are interested in?

- Are you happy to proceed?
- Very often you won't even get to this stage, your patient will already have indicated much earlier in the conversation that they are happy to proceed.

(Remember to document this conversation clearly in your records as well).

Key Points of The P.A.C.E Method:

This takes a lot of practice.

"Luck is when preparation meets opportunity".

Successful business people, who make a lot of money, also help a lot of people with their products and services, are those who are prepared to practice and prepared to close the sale.

Dentistry is no different.

Chapter 11

Summary

Step 1
Timing is Key

→ At the current appointment
→ Careful with your language
→ Don't rush this process, slow down

Step 2
Demonstrate the Problem

→ A Demonstration is better than a presentation
→ Discuss the problem first, not the solution
→ Invest in an intra oral camera

Step 3
Contrast Principle

→ Compare the various realistic options in terms of what is involved
→ Offer your recommendation
→ Features, benefits, outcomes and transformations

→ Don't mention the money before this stage!

Step 4
'The Money Chat'

→ Compare the investment involved with each option
→ Avoid discounting
→ Offer your recommendation
→ Be clear on the money involved, no ambiguity
→ Remember the price is only _a_ factor, not _the_ factor

[Handling Objections]

→ Translate objections into questions
→ Handle an objection before it is even raised (or else immediately)
→ Practice, practice, practice

Step 5
Question Time

→ Ask better quality question
→ Listening and observing is as important as asking
→ Think about when to used Open vs Closed types

Step 6
Take Action

→ 'Closing' or finishing the conversation is key
→ Don't sell, allow patients to buy
→ Book the return journey

Remember – we're are simply treating people how we would want to be treated ourselves.

We would want, and deserve, to hear all the relevant options.

We wouldn't want our financial status to be assumed or what we could afford pre-judged.

But, sadly, as dentists we are not always taught how to do this.

Much of dentistry is focused on the clinical, hands-on aspect.

Which is great.

But, as you and I know, dentistry is such a 'people-profession' we need to be able to talk to be, put them at ease, feel comfortable doing our dentistry in our own surgeries.

You need a structure, a template.

You already have these for the clinical aspects.

You would never place a composite restoration without etching and bonding.

Or maybe even local anaesthetic.

But the order to that structure is so important.

No point in administering LA after you have prepared the cavity. Or etching the tooth after the bond.

Now I know that is obvious to us both – but you know what I mean by this example.

You have the clinical structures and methods you follow, perhaps even on autopilot now.

But you did spend several years in dental school after all.

You now need to take the time to invest in yourself with this training and learn (or re-learn) a communication structure.

Practice makes permanent, it does not make perfect

Both you and your patients will benefit immediately.

It's not about money.

It's about people.

Really high-quality communication, in dentistry, has a kind of beauty to it.

Where the science of dentistry and the art of communication combine.

Do let us know how you get on.

Wishing You Every Success,

Leonard & Derek

Dr Leonard J Maguire
BDS MFDS RCSEd MFGDP MDTFEd AFFMLM LL.M MBA CMgr
MCMI PG Dip. Med. Ed. FICD

Dr Derek J Maguire
BDS MDTFEd FFGDP(UK) FDS RCPS(Glas) FICD

General Dental Surgeons
Founders of The Dentists Academy
- "The Complete Business Toolkit for Dentists in General Practice"

P.S. From the desk of Leonard Maguire:

When I think about some of the most successful people, and dentists, that I know and work with, they all have one specific trait in common.

They know exactly what they want to say, right before they say it.

Then… they come straight out with it.

That sounds obvious I know.

But, very often, it is misunderstood.

Follow a structure, a template.

There is no confusion or guesswork.

Use a labyrinth, not a maze.

You can learn to become a powerful and effective communicator.

No-one is born with the ability to communicate effectively. It is a learned skill.

The more you can co-ordinate all three of these parts, the greater the impact your message will have.

And in turn, the more likely they will be to fully understand what you are saying (valid, informed consent) and react how you want them to – enabling you to provide the best treatment you can for them.

Here's a good way to think about this:

Consider the difference between a labyrinth and a maze.

When you enter a maze, you don't know where you are going.

There is no direction.

No known final destination.

Chaos ensues.

Contrast that with a labyrinth, where there is only one pathway that you can take, to get to where you need.

You end up in one place, one outcome.

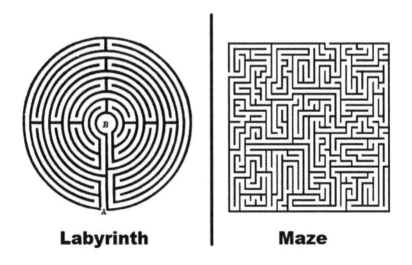

Labyrinth | **Maze**

You need systems, structures and processes when you discuss treatment options, fees and plans comfortably and with confidence.

This can be learned.

Don't work with a maze – confusion and chaos result.

If you don't have clarity with your thoughts and words, how can you expect your patients to understand clearly.

If you'd like to learn more about using labyrinths…

Visit www.thedentistsacademy.com and download your FREE copy of report:

'The 7 Big Mistakes Dentists Unwittingly Make, Exposing Them to Expensive Lawsuits'

BONUS Chapter 12

Building Genuine Rapport

As a fellow dentist, I'm sure we'll agree, building rapport is one of the most important topics to learn as much as you can about.

People tend to buy things from people they know, trust and like.

People don't tend to complain about people they know, trust and like.

The same is generally true of dentists and patients.

Haven't you met a salesperson that you just 'click' with.

There's natural rapport, you just want to buy from them.

Here's the deal…

Words make up 7% of communication – i.e. what you say

Tonality = how you're saying it equates to 30%

(but 70% if over the phone – important if training or re-training your reception team)

And whilst most people focus on the words…

The most important aspect of communication is the physiology, being around 63% (approx. figures).

The most important part is how you're using your body in the interaction.

So, we're agreed, developing rapport is key.

It will enable patients to know, trust, and in all probability, like us.

And in doing so, ensure they are much more engaged and open-minded to the treatments we suggest.

All resulting in the best possible dentistry being carried out.

Win-win.

General business studies have shown that 80% of all 'sales' are based on a prospect *liking and trusting* the sales person.

Not based on how much it costs.

Not even if it is the best product or service.

Based on a prospect liking and trusting the sales person.

So how do we create this environment with our patients?

First off, you want to be **matching and mirroring**.

This simply means that you align yourself in some way with another person.

So you are like them.

People tend to like people who are like them.

And tend not to like people who are not like them.

Simple (but not always easy).

This includes the following areas:

- **Mood**
- **Voice**
- **Speed of talking**
- **Pitch**
- **Habitual key phrases**
- **Movements**
- **Breathing**

Mood

So, the first thing you want to match and mirror about a person is their **mood**.

What are typical sales people taught?

Go in there and be positive!

Be energetic, be positive!

But what they don't always realise is you need to meet people where they are *first*, before you lead them to where you want them *to go*.

How about a really positive person you've met?

Now imagine you've woken up and you're in a bad mood.

You're like "urgh".

Then you've got Tom Positive coming in...

"Hey man, how's it going, what a great day?"

Where do you feel like telling them to go?

If they're happy, be happy with them, if they're sad be with them in it.

Recently, I saw a patient whose sister had very suddenly and unexpectantly passed away at Christmas time.

She was only 33 years old.

He walked into the room, hugged me and thanked me for the sympathy card I had sent.

That was never going to be an easy conversation, seeing him for the first time again since this tragedy.

But strangely, it doesn't mean there was no rapport.

We just chatted it through and how he and the family were coping etc.

Remember, we're in healthcare and part of a caring profession.

It's not always about the last £/$/€ earned.

So, match their mood and state of mind as best you can.

Meet people where they are.

We are in a very privileged position to be able to interact with people, as patients, every day.

Ironically, I feel that sometimes patients feel more able to 'open up' to their dentist than the medical doctor.

Think about it, normally people only tend to see their medical doctor when something is wrong/sore.

Whereas we, as dentists, have patients coming to see us routinely for maintenance or check-ups – and leave with no issues.

As such, they can feel more comfortable in the dental surgery environment, sharing stories about their work, family, studies etc.

All building rapport and trust.

When a patient does share something personal with you, make a small note somewhere in their records, such as:

- Holiday in Florida
- Favourite team Manchester United
- New dog called Sam
- Moving to a new house
- Child starting school

By taking an interest in this way, you will automatically have areas to discuss when they next come back.

And how impressed they will be.

These facts can be difficult to remember when you are seeing 20-30 patients each day!

So simply make a small note on their chart to remind you to ask how they got on with "training the new dog" or "the big house move" etc.

Voice

Another key thing to match and mirror is their **voice**.

How they're speaking?

I talk fast now.

But not as fast as I used to!

I remember when I moved up to the North Coast in Northern Ireland for my Dental Foundation Training year.

I was talking really fast like back home.

People would just be looking at me like – "where did you come from?"

Here's the problem - if I'm not like them, their natural reaction is not to like me as quickly.

So, there's different parts of the voice you can match and mirror.

Speed

One of them is **Speed**.

How quickly the person is speaking?

If you're talking to someone and they're talking really, really slowly, you want to slow down your voice too.

Why?

To develop rapport with them.

If they're talking really quickly you want to pick up the pace.

Pitch

The **pitch** is important – talking like you or maybe a little softer.

Got to match it.

If they're talking softly and you're, perhaps unwittingly, discussing a treatment plan in a fast, loud manner?

Remember some people may say this is manipulative.

And it's not.

There are good ways and bad ways to use these tactics.

It's only to be used to help patients gain what they truly need.

Rapport is a key, key concept – you're not going to be able to help anybody without it.

Habitual Key Phrases

Also, consider any **habitual key phrases** that they use.

For example, use *their* language.

There is emotion tied to these words.

They feel it inside.

Especially if they are using a word in a positive way.

Not necessarily something that you would say all the time.

Remember, in Northern Ireland we say things like "what's the craic?".

Which translates to "how are you?".

Movements

Next - match and mirror their physiology – how they **move their body**.

This happens naturally when people have rapport.

Next time you go out to dinner, take a moment and observe the people around you.

People who are in rapport and those who are not.

Even with the person you are with.

You will notice you are sitting the exact same way.

Usually this is unconsciously happening.

Then, if their legs are crossed, you do the same.

Not at exactly the same time (don't want to be creepy!).

Even if they cross their arms – this body language might mean this is uncomfortable.

Perhaps they've misunderstood or don't believe what you're saying.

Meet people **where** they are.

Be careful though.

Sometimes when someone scratches their nose, they just have an itch!

Meet them where they are.

Match and mirror.

Then once rapport has been developed, they will uncross their arms.

You'll feel it – just test it.

Switch from matching and mirroring to pacing and leading.

Meaning you are going to follow me!

You'll see you are now leading them.

It feels good to be in rapport.

Breathing

Next – their **breathing**.

When two people are really in rapport, they are breathing in exactly the same way.

Just watch.

This is extremely powerful.

Remember – the reason you are doing this is so you can make an impact on them and improve their life in some way.

And also remember - don't do all of these at once!

It should be invisible.

It should not be obvious that this is happening.

A tactic known is a tactic blown!

Just think…

If I were offering a particular treatment plan to a blind patient?

A deaf patient?

You'd have to change your presentation to get your points across.

Of course, the most important thing in developing rapport – what we talked about at the start – is not the <u>technique</u> but the <u>feeling</u> it creates.

You truly care about serving your patient.

That comes through naturally when it is genuine.

These techniques are used to underline the most important thing.

Which is that you truly want to serve and help this person.

Because you have associated what exactly this product or service does for them.

And the difference it makes to their life.

Now, BEWARE!

Once you have created rapport, you want to maintain it.

So how would you inadvertently get out of rapport immediately?

There's one word, that if you use it, you kill rapport.

It's… **"BUT"**.

<u>Example:</u>

Imagine you're going to ask someone on a date.

And then you hear, "You know, you're a really nice guy, **but**..."

You know what's coming after 'but'... BAD

What are you saying when you use the word 'but'?

"Yes, but…"

What you're doing is basically saying, 'no you're wrong'

And you negate everything that comes before it.

Here's what you could use instead of BUT.

Maintain rapport by agreeing with them - not necessarily just agreeing.

But making a statement that maintains rapport.

e.g. "I understand how you feel", "I can appreciate"

"it is expensive, and…"

"I agree" (if you do) – be truthful.

Don't say it if you don't agree.

But you can agree if it is expensive!

I use that all the time

It's ok to be way more expensive than everybody else

Sometimes "reassuringly expensive".

"I appreciate what you're saying, and…"

e.g. If someone throws the "it's too expensive" objection at you.

"You know, I can appreciate that, it is expensive, and… here's why you still need it."

You see the difference compared to "It is expensive, but…"?

You've contradicted what the patient's said if you use the word 'but'.

"I can appreciate that, and you're right these are expensive, and the reason they are is that… I can absolutely recommend this is the best type of filling for your tooth"

Do you see how I maintain rapport with them?

I'm not arguing with them.

You're using their energy, maintaining rapport.

Once you have developed rapport with them,

Then you go on to pacing and leading them

Then they start following you.

So, if you speed up your voice a little bit, they'll speed up their voice a little bit.

Have a go for yourself, you'll be amazed.

Here's **your assignment** on this!

- Develop rapport using matching and mirroring.
- Then test it (by doing something different).
- If they follow you, move on to pacing and leading.
- If they don't follow you, you need to develop rapport further.
- But this can happen very, very quickly.
- Literally in as little as 4 minutes – if you're doing it right.
- You'll be amazed.

Day 1 = Match and mirror people's body language. Even if they're across the room.

Day 2 = use vocal quality

Day 3 = match and mirror the person's mood

Day 4 = the most powerful one, consider the person's breathing.

I'd urge you to try this out and aim to make these techniques personal to you.

Take what feels good to you.

Everything must be congruent in what you do.

Before I go…

I thought I'd share a **classic sales technique, the "Feel Felt Found" Method.**

It's very simple and effective, as below:

- ○ *I understand how you **feel**.*
- ○ *In fact, many of my happiest patients **felt** the same way.*
- ○ *And here's what they **found** – they got this benefit (a), benefit (b)…*

Can you think of a patient could use this with immediately to help demonstrate the true value in what you can provide?

Message from
Leonard and Derek

Attention: Fellow General Dental Surgeon

The Dentists Academy provides real-life help and solutions for you about the business of dentistry.

Whether you are just starting out in dental school, recently graduated, hoping to buy your own practice, or indeed are already a Principal – here is the information that can help you thrive financially.

These are very challenging times in dentistry.

Patient expectations are at an all-time high.

Financial strains have never been tighter.

Complaints and litigation are increasing.

However, it's the most rewarding career in the world when you conquer these stressful aspects.

Let's get started on your journey to success together.

We are passionate about providing the highest quality dentistry for patients.

And so, we equip you with the business tools to ensure you are able to do this.

Remember - this is different.

And the recognition that many of the struggles dentists face are not necessarily clinical matters, rather:

- √ **Discussing fees with confidence**
- √ **Communicating treatment plans with patients**
- √ **Handling complaints**
- √ **Managing expectations**
- √ **Managing stress**
- √ **Effective time management**

So, we are going to share with you, our tried and tested proven ideas, through our **Members' Monthly Web Meets** (recorded and stored for you) and online environment.

Here's the biggest difference… **we are dentists and practice owners in General Practice too.**

Often people don't need to be told what action to take. Instead, it is the strategies on <u>how to do so</u> that's required.

Hard work will be involved – no doubt about it.

However, the rewards are outstanding.

Your Membership gives you an <u>unfair advantage</u> over the rest of the field.

Time for action...

You know you need to provide the dentistry that:

- **Your patients deserve**
- **You enjoy doing**
- **You can be proud of**

We're here to help you avoid the pitfalls that can so easily and quickly arise in dentistry and continually provide the ideas, methods and tools so you can succeed – in the business of dentistry.

Innovate, don't invent. The self-made wealthy know that it's taking good ideas and making them better that creates real wealth. Un-wealthy believe you need an all-new big idea.

Wishing You Every Success

Leonard and Derek Maguire

Founders
The Dentists Academy

P.P.S. If you ardently believe in what you're doing / 'selling' as a dentist and want to positively impact more patients with your product or service, you might be a perfect fit for our Private Client Program.

If you're interested, send me an email to me at leonard@thedentistsacademy. com with the subject line, "Private Client Info," and I'll give you the details.

Action Notes:

_____

_____

_____

_____

_____

_____

_____

_____

_____

_____

_____

_____

Action Notes:

_____

_____

_____

_____

_____

_____

_____

_____

_____

_____

_____

_____

Action Notes:

_____

_____

_____

_____

_____

_____

_____

_____

_____

_____

_____

_____

_____

Action Notes:

_____

_____

_____

_____

_____

_____

_____

_____

_____

_____

_____

_____

Action Notes:

Testimonials

"Lenny taught me how to communicate effectively with patients and discuss a range of treatment options with a logical and patient centred approach. He helped improve my confidence levels and made the transition from university into the working world a lot easier with the skills he has given me."

\- Dr Hannah M

"One to one sessions with Leonard have been a game-changer. Bridging the gap between clinical knowledge and business know-how to achieve the most from your patient interactions. Leonard's advice simply just makes sense – he pulls the obvious into view and sets a path to improve communication, time management and isn't afraid to tackle the taboo of money matters. I've always left feeling enthused and equipped to do my best for my patients and benefit as a self-employed associate dentist."

\- Dr Lyndsey McM

"Leonard and Derek breakdown the 'business of dentistry' and provide ethical, effective and practical approaches to help you provide the best for your patients."

\- Dr Chris M

"How to properly communicate treatment options and discussing fees is an area which is completely avoided in dental school, leaving dentists with the daunting and uncertain task of self-education once they are operating in the real world.

My solution was The Dentists Academy.

The Dentists Academy has trained me how to effectively deliver all treatment options with confidence and exactly how to have "the money chat" with patients. The results are better care for my patients, an increase in earnings and a solid standing dento-legally."

- Dr David K

"Leonard's advice and coaching for Dental Foundation Training was invaluable for improving my interview skills and building my confidence. He taught me how to structure my answers for the interview scenarios, so I could apply it to any question I was asked. Thanks to his excellent coaching I gained a place in my first-choice scheme."

- Dr Shannon C

"From the outset of my career I quickly realised that Dentistry was so much more than just the practical knowledge acquired during undergraduate training. I soon recognised the need for business knowledge and financial planning as a self-employed Dentist. The one-to-one and CPD training with Derek and Leonard has been invaluable to me in developing these skills. Following training and continuous support, I now feel better equipped in managing the business aspects of Dentistry."

- Dr Rebecca McC

About the Authors

Dr. Leonard J Maguire

BDS MFDS RcsEd MFGDP MDTFEd AFFMLM LL.M MBA Cmgr MCMI PG Dip. Med.Ed. FICD

Leonard gained his Bachelor of Dental Surgery from Queen's University Belfast in 2014, with Degree Plus.

Prior to this, he ranked 1st in the UK in Dental Foundation Training out of over 1200 applicants in 2014.

Since that time, he has spent a significant amount of time working clinically and studying at weekends and evenings.

He gained his Membership of the Faculty of Dental Surgery with the Royal College of Surgeons of Edinburgh and has also be awarded Membership to the Faculty of Dental Trainers with the Royal College of Surgeons of Edinburgh as well.

He is also a Member of the Faculty of General Dental Practice with the Royal College of Surgeons of England.

He holds a Master of Business Administration with the University of Liverpool and a further Master of Law in Medical Law and Ethics from the University of Edinburgh.

Furthermore, he has been awarded an Associate Fellowship with the Faculty of Medical Leadership and Management and is an Associate Member of the Faculty of Forensic and Legal Medicine.

He also holds a Post-Graduate Diploma in Medical Education from the University of Dundee and is an Internal Examiner for the National Examining Board for Dental Nurses (NEBDN).

He is a Chartered Manager and Member of the Chartered Management Institute and holds Membership to the Institute of Clinical Research.

He now divides his time between "wet-fingered" dentistry as a General Dental Surgeon, mentoring and coaching GDPs, and as Operations Director within his family owned group of 10 General Dental Practices in Northern Ireland.

Leonard has also been named as a Fellow of the International College of Dentists.

General Dental Council No: 250765

Dr. Derek J Maguire

BDS MDTFEd RCSEd FFGDP(UK) FDS RCPS(Glas) FICD

Derek qualified with his Bachelor of Dental Surgery from Queen's University Belfast in 1987.

Having been awarded Membership to the Faculty of Dental Trainers with the Royal College of Surgeons of Edinburgh (MDTFEd RCSEd) in 2017 and also sits on their Executive Committee.

Derek also holds a Fellowship with the Faculty of General Dental Practice through the Royal College of Surgeons of England (FFGDP) and acts as Facilitator and Assessor for those hoping to gain Fellowship with the College.

Derek is the Principal Dentist and owner of DJ Maguire & Associates Ltd, his General Dental Practice group, which he founded in 1989. It has grown to some 45 Associate Dentists and additional staff who provide their services to approximately 55,000 NHS registered patients, across 10 separate sites in Northern Ireland.

Derek has recently been awarded a Fellowship of Dental Surgery qualification, FDS RCPS(Glas). This is a prestigious qualification awarded by the Royal College of Physicians and Surgeons of Glasgow, in recognition of his contribution to General Dental Practice in Northern Ireland.

Derek also holds Membership to the Institute of Clinical Research (MICR) and has been named as a Fellow of the International College of Dentists (FICD).

General Dental Council No: 62393